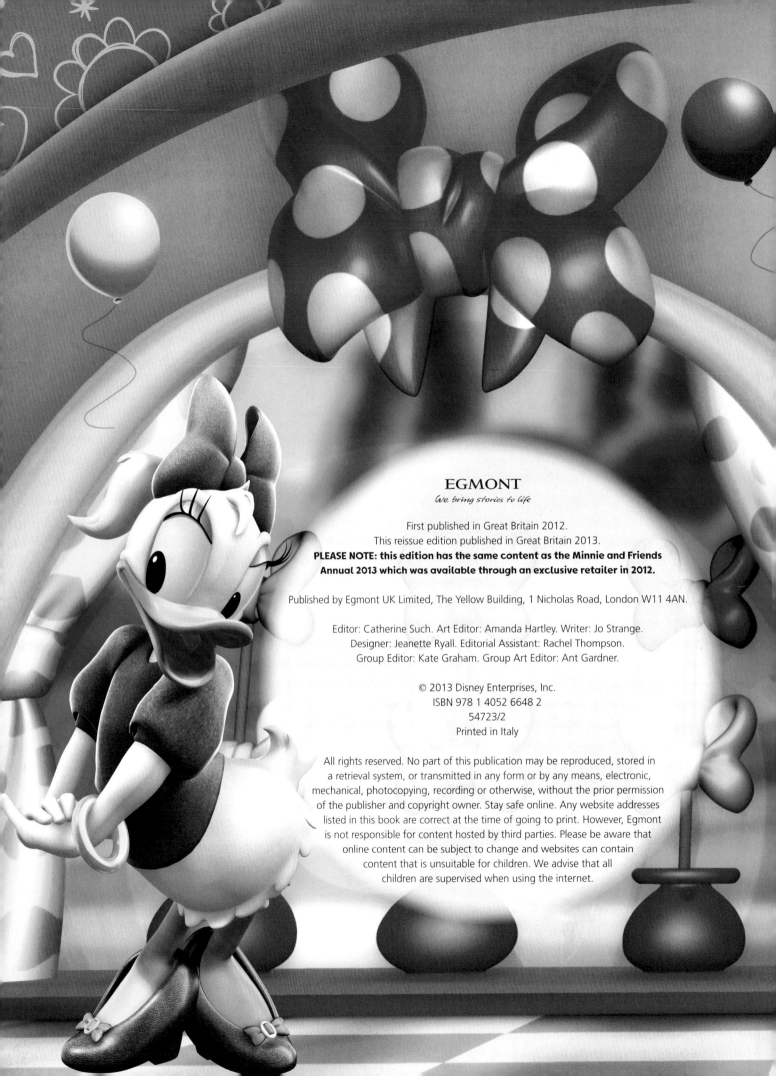

EGMONT

We bring stories to life

First published in Great Britain 2012.
This reissue edition published in Great Britain 2013.
**PLEASE NOTE: this edition has the same content as the Minnie and Friends
Annual 2013 which was available through an exclusive retailer in 2012.**

Published by Egmont UK Limited, The Yellow Building, 1 Nicholas Road, London W11 4AN.

Editor: Catherine Such. Art Editor: Amanda Hartley. Writer: Jo Strange.
Designer: Jeanette Ryall. Editorial Assistant: Rachel Thompson.
Group Editor: Kate Graham. Group Art Editor: Ant Gardner.

© 2013 Disney Enterprises, Inc.
ISBN 978 1 4052 6648 2
54723/2
Printed in Italy

Disney MINNIE

ANNUAL 2014

This annual belongs to

....

Write your name here.

Contents

Meet Minnie

Say hello to Minnie Mouse. She's the sweetest, kindest, most stylish mouse you'll ever meet!

Minnie Facts

Full name: Minerva Mouse
Parents: Marcus and Margie Mouse
Boyfriend: Mickey Mouse
Best friends: Daisy Duck, Clarabelle Cow

Fashion Favourites

Favourite colour: pink
Favourite pattern: polka dots
Best accessory: pink polka-dot bows!

Minnie hobbies ...

* Dancing
* Dressing-up
* Gardening
* Singing

Minnie loves ...

* Looking after her friends
* Spending time with Mickey
* Running her shop
* Experimenting with new fashions

Minnie

Who is Mickey Mouse's girfriend? Trace over her name, then colour the bows.

9

Minnie's Friends

There is nothing Minnie enjoys more than spending time with her friends. Let's meet them all ...

Mickey Mouse

Mickey is Minnie's Prince Charming. When the two of them get together, they make a great team and always take care of one another.

Donald Duck

Donald is a good friend to Minnie. Although he gets cross easily, Minnie knows Donald has a heart of gold.

Pluto

Mickey's loyal dog, Pluto, is a big softie. Minnie likes to tickle Pluto behind the ears, but she doesn't like it when he gives her a big, wet lick!

Answer on page 67.

Goofy

Goofy can be very clumsy at times, but Minnie wouldn't have her kind, well-meaning friend any other way!

Daisy Duck

Daisy is Minnie's best friend. Minnie and Daisy love spending time together and swapping lots of fashion tips.

Can you tell which friend is hiding behind Pluto's kennel?

Mickey **Donald**

Tick the correct circle.

Figaro

Figaro is Minnie's pet cat. She loves her cuddly companion!

Two by Two

Minnie and Daisy are riding a two-seater bicycle. Can you spot six differences in picture b?

a

b

Colour a flower each time you spot a difference.

Answers on page 67.

Friends Forever

Complete the picture of Minnie and Daisy with your prettiest coloured pens.

Use the little picture to help you.

13

The New Puppy

Minnie is taking her new puppy for a nice long walk. Who will they meet along the way?

Follow the path with a pen and trace the numbers as you meet each friend.

14

How many paw prints can you count?

Happy Faces

Can you draw lines to link each of Minnie's friends to their matching shadow?

The first one has been done for you.

Answers on page 67.

Find a Friend

Try and find the names of Minnie's four friends in the word wheel. We've found the first one for you.

GOOFY

DAISY

DONALD

DRXAQRLOPEMWACPLUTO
DONALDRXAQRLOPEMWACPLUTO
SVGOOFYAEKWHSEIUPDAISY
TABSVGOOFYAEKWH
SKTABSVGOOFY
WAESKTAB
RMWAE
RMW
SEIUPDAISYUAGBWFULSZDONALD
EASPLB

Tick off the friends as you find their names.

PLUTO

17

Answers on page 67.

Special

1. One morning, bright and early,
The postman came to call.
"1, 2, 3, 4, 5 parcels."
Mickey counted them all!

2. Just then, Mickey's friends arrived,
Handy Helper let them in.
"My, what a lot of parcels!" said Minnie,
"I don't know where to begin!"

3. There was a parcel for everyone,
The friends opened them with glee.
Except poor Donald that is,
"Oh, there isn't one for me."

4. When Donald left the Clubhouse,
He was feeling rather blue.
But Goofy had an idea,
"Let's give Donald a parcel, too!"

Delivery

5 Handy Helper was at the ready,
To help with the surprise.
He held an envelope for Daisy,
And she blew a kiss inside.

6 Goofy wanted to put in giggles,
So, he needed something funny.
Handy Helper had a plan.
He tickled Goofy's tummy!

Something sweet!

7 Lastly, it was Minnie's turn,
She wanted to add something sweet,
So Handy Helper made a cake,
Oh, Donald was in for a treat!

Thanks for my parcel!

8 Then later at the Clubhouse,
A special delivery arrived.
The parcel was for Donald,
And there was lots of love inside!

Passion for Fashion

Minnie just loves fashion! Complete these stylish puzzles.

Pattern Crazy

Look carefully. Can you pick out the pattern that matches the one on Minnie's dress? Tick the right box.

a

b

c

d

e

f

a

b

c

d

e

Bags Galore

Tick the heart next to Minnie's favourite bag. It's the one that isn't part of a matching pair.

High Style

Can you decorate Daisy's bag with some pretty colours?

Answers on page 67.

Minnie's Dress

Which dress is Minnie dreaming about? Look at her thought bubble, then find the dress to match the shapes in it.

a

b

c

d

Trace over the shapes!

circle   square   triangle   heart

Answer on page 67.

Fashion Model

Give Minnie some fashion colours to make her look super-stylish on the catwalk.

Colourful Accessories

How many accessories are there in each group? Count them up and write your answers in the hearts.

Daisy is helping Minnie sort out her accessories into colour groups, so she can easily find things to match her outfits.

a

Yellow

Trace over the words.

1 2 3 4 5

b

Blue

c

Red

d

Purple

Circle your favourite accessory in each group!

6 7 8 9 10

Minnie's Designs

Minnie is designing some new outfits. Help her draw the dress patterns on to the fabric by tracing over the dotted lines.

Put a tick by your favourite pattern.

Draw a picture of yourself in your favourite dress.

Fashion Shoot

Minnie is taking photographs of Daisy. Can you find the two pictures that are exactly the same?

a

b

Tick the hearts to show your answer.

c

d

e

Answer on page 67.

Nurse Minnie

When Minnie hears that Goofy is feeling poorly, she knows just what to do ...

One morning, Minnie set off in a hurry to find Mickey. **KNOCK! KNOCK! KNOCK!** she tapped impatiently on the Clubhouse door.

When Mickey opened the door, Minnie stepped inside, shaking her head and twitching her nose with **worry** 😦.

"What's the matter, Minnie?" asked Mickey.

"It's Goofy," Minnie explained. "He has a terrible cold. I really want to take him something to make him feel better, but I'm stuck for ideas."

"Why don't we make him a get well card?" suggested Mickey.

Minnie thought for a moment.

"A card is nice but it won't help his cold." Just then, she had an idea. "I know! I'll make him some of my special, feel-better **Minniestrone soup!**"

"Great idea! I'll help you. How many **tomatoes** do we need?" asked Mickey.

"One, two, three!" cried Minnie, excitedly. "And then we need **onions, carrots,** some **herbs** and a sprinkle of my secret ingredient!"

In no time at all, the soup was ready and smelling delicious.

Minnie and Mickey set off through the woods, carrying the pot of soup in a **basket.**

"This **Minniestrone soup** will have Goofy feeling better in no time," said Minnie.

"Oh, did someone just say **soup?**" said a **booming** voice.

Minnie and Mickey jumped into the air with fright.

"Who said that?" squeaked Mickey.

"It was ME!" said Pete. "Can I have some of your **soup?**"

Minnie explained to Pete that the soup was for Goofy.

"He has a terrible cold," Mickey added.

"I have a terrible cold, too," said Pete. "Ah-choo!"

"You haven't got a cold, you're just pretending so you can take Goofy's soup!" cried Mickey.

Pete stamped crossly towards Minnie and snatched the **basket** out of her hands. "You can't catch me up this **tree!**" he yelled, as he started to climb.

Minnie and Mickey quickly called **Toodles** for help. "We need a ladder …" said Mickey, "… and quick!"

Toodles gave a ladder to Mickey, who speedily climbed up towards naughty Pete.

"**Tickle! Tickle! Tickle!**" giggled Mickey, reaching out and tickling Pete's feet. "Hey, cut that out!" giggled Pete, dropping the **basket.**

Minnie caught the **basket** and **Toodles** handed her a pair of roller-skates. Minnie quickly put them on and skated off before Pete could climb down from the tree. "See you later, Pete!" she cried.

Goofy was very pleased to see Minnie skate up to his bedside. "I've brought you some of my special **Minniestrone soup,**" said Minnie. "Mickey helped me make it."

Minnie poured the **soup** into a bowl and while Goofy started eating it, she told him about their adventure with Pete. When they got to the feet-tickling part, Goofy laughed so much, he forgot to sneeze!

"Thank you, Nurse Minnie," said Goofy, as he took more spoonfuls of the delicious **soup.** "I feel so much better already. Your **Minniestrone** soup really is special!"

THE END

Draw the Fruits

Using the panel to help you, can you draw the missing fruit in each row?

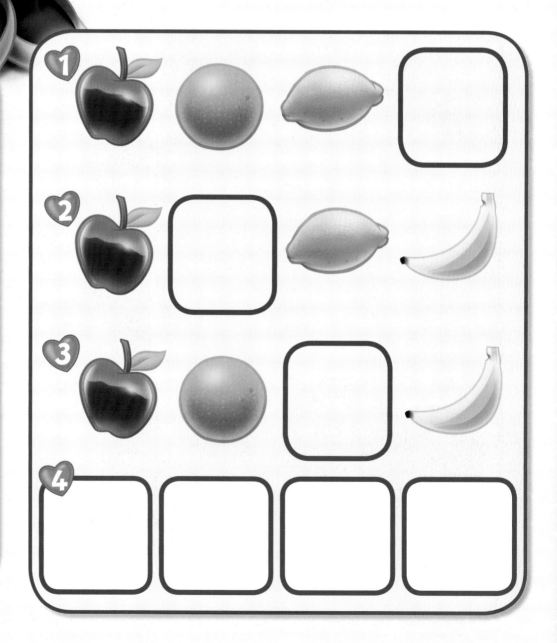

Answers on page 67.

Special Treat

Minnie is tucking into a slice of birthday cake!

Can you colour the picture?

1

2

3

Follow the number key to help you choose which colours to use.

33

What's Cooking?

Minnie and Mickey are stirring up a treat in the kitchen! Draw a line to link each pair of cooking items.

Which one doesn't have a match?

Answers on page 67.

Cute Cakes

Minnie adores cupcakes, but what flavour is her favourite?

Follow the path from Minnie to find out.

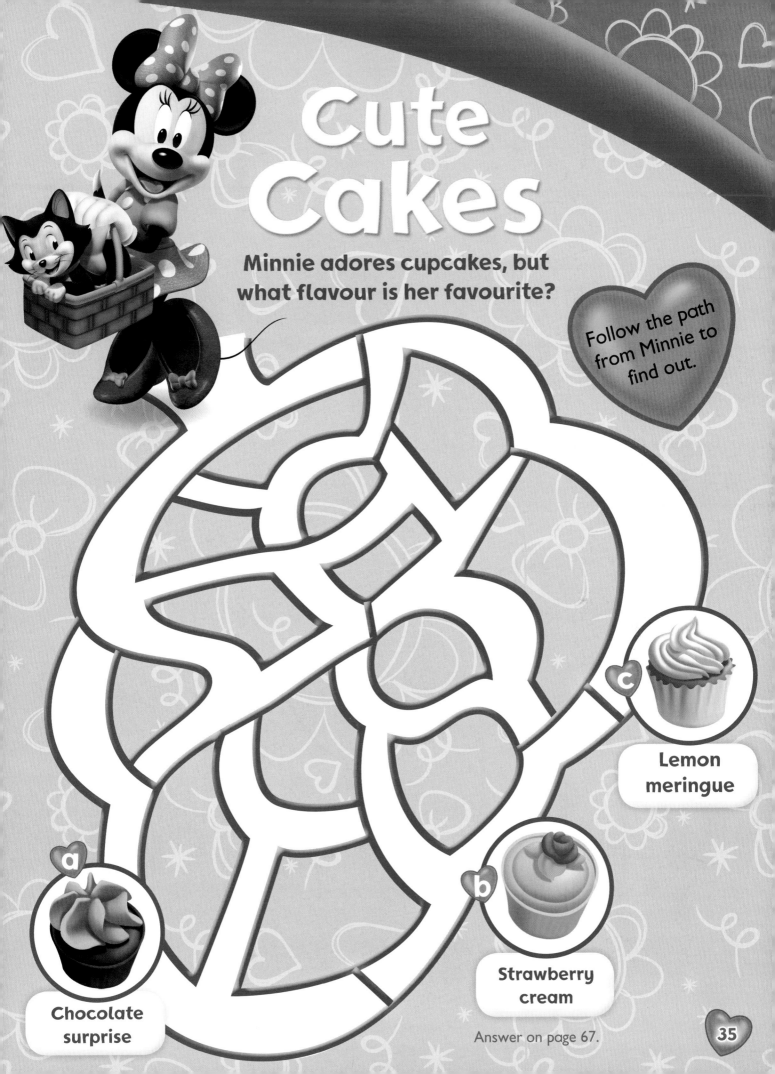

c Lemon meringue

b Strawberry cream

a Chocolate surprise

Answer on page 67.

Foodie Favourites

Minnie and her pals are snacking on their favourite foods. Can you complete the puzzles?

1 Ice cream is Minnie's favourite. Circle the BIGGEST ice cream sundae.

a

b

c

d

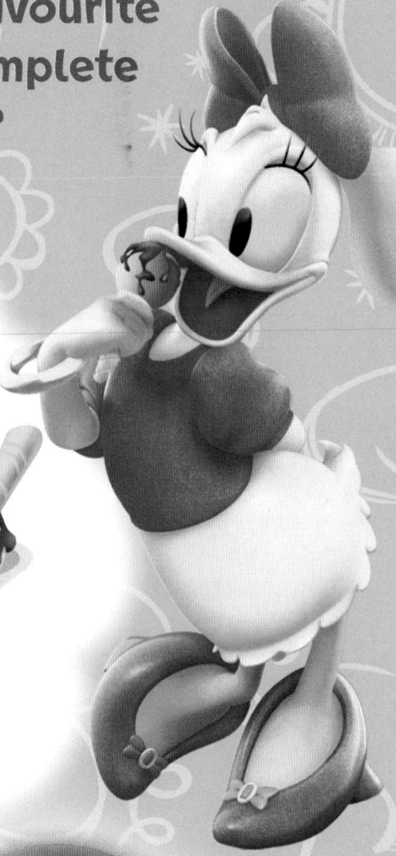

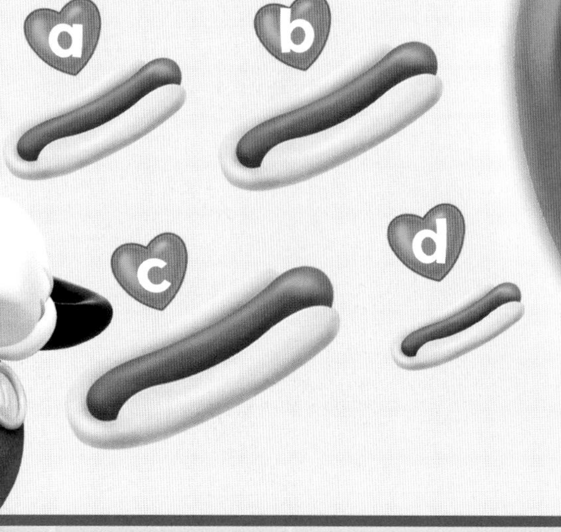

2 Mickey just loves hotdogs! Circle the SMALLEST hot dog.

a

b

c

d

3

Pluto likes to chew his bones.

Circle both the BIGGEST and the SMALLEST bone.

a

b

c

d

Colour Minnie so she can enjoy her hot chocolate!

b

c

a

d

4

Minnie loves hot chocolate.

Circle the BIGGEST hot chocolate.

37

Answers on page 67.

Point to Figaro the cat.

Now trace Minnie's dance steps as she twirls around!

START

FINISH

Answer on page 67.

39

Dotty about Dancing

Help Daisy join the dots from 1 to 10 to complete the music box.

6
7
8
5
4
9
3
•10
2
1

When you've finished, hum a lovely tune for Minnie to twirl around to!

Nice Moves

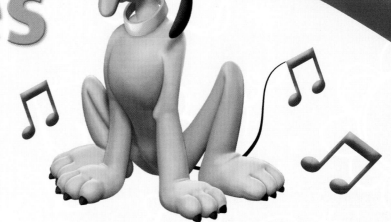

Minnie and her friends are practising their best dance moves. Tick the odd one out in each row.

1
a
b
c
d

2
a
b
c
d

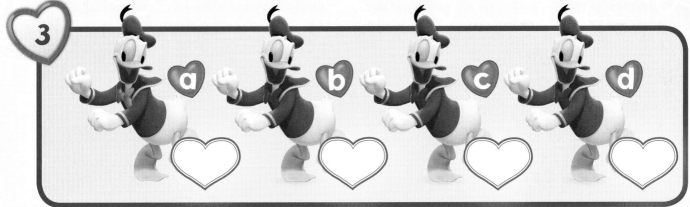

3
a
b
c
d

Answers on page 67.

Dance Partners

Minnie needs a dance partner! Can you draw a path through the maze from Minnie to Mickey? Then lead Daisy to Donald, too.

Too Many Shoes

Can you read the story? When you come to a picture, check the picture key and say the word out loud.

One morning, visited in a bit of a panic. "Oh,

," she said, "I wonder if you could help me? I need some

 to wear to the ball tonight, but I can't find any to match my

outfit!" "Don't worry," said . "I have shoes for every occasion.

You can never have too many shoes!" dashed over to her

 and looked inside. Eventually, at the very back of the

she found the she was looking for. "Ah, here they are. These

are the ones you need." opened the and pulled out

a pair of pretty . "Oh, my, they're perfect!" cried

. "Would you mind if I borrowed them?" "Of course, not,"

said , "although they are not quite perfect yet ..."

carefully sewed some on to the front of each shoe.

"There! That looks better!" she giggled. The matched those on

the ball gown had chosen to wear. "Oh, thank you," said

 . "Ahh, but we're not finished yet," said . She took

another look in her and found some silky material. The pattern

on the material matched the pattern on the . In no time at

all, transformed the material into a beautiful for

to wear in her hair. was delighted. "I think you're right,

 , " she said. "It's true that you can never have too many

shoes ... or pearls ... or bows!" and they both laughed.

The End

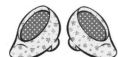 

Keep Dancing!

Minnie is bopping along to her favourite songs.

Use your favourite pens to colour this happy picture.

Sport Crazy

Minnie and Daisy are cheerleading!

Write your answers in the boxes, then trace over the numbers below.

How many of each of the items below can you count in the picture?

1 2 3 4 5

Answers on page 68.

Out and About

Minnie and her friends are enjoying the fresh air.

Can you spot the objects below in the scene? Tick a box as you find each one.

Add some colour to the beautiful butterflies.

 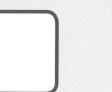

Places to Go

Minnie and Daisy are taking a car journey, but before they set off you'll need to complete the picture.

Can you work out which jigsaw piece goes where? Write the letters in the hearts.

a

b

c

d

1

2

3

4

Answers on page 68.

On the Move

Daisy is thinking about going to visit Pluto.

Give Pluto some colour, then trace over Daisy's trail as she skips away!

MICKEY PARK

How many roses are there?

Answer on page 68.

Minnie's Day

It sure is busy being Minnie! Come and join her as she goes about her day.

Morning

In the morning, Minnie played tennis with Mickey.

Score Card

4 5

Mickey **Minnie**

1
Can you trace the numbers on the score card? Who won the most games?

Lunch time

After lunch, Minnie did a spot of shopping.

2
Shade the dotted sections to see what she bought.

Afternoon

In the afternoon, Minnie baked a delicious pie for her friends to share.

3

To find out what fruit she used, cross off the letters that appear twice.

i j
s p e o a
o i j c h
m n s m n

Evening

In the evening, Minnie settled down to write in her diary.

*Dear Diary,
The thing I enjoyed most was ....*

....

....

4

What part of her day do you think she enjoyed the most?

Flower

Minnie wants her garden to be full of flowers come springtime. Can you help her plant some flower bulbs?

Tulip

Daffodil

Daisy

Fun

Trace the trails to plant the seeds, then colour the flowers with your favourite pens.

55

Colourful Flowers

Minnie's flowerbed is looking pretty.

How many of each type of flower can you count? Write your answers below.

Trace over the numbers in the row, then use them to help you.

a   **b**   **c**   **d**

1 2 3 4 5

Answers on page 68.

Hello Butterfly!

Minnie has made some new friends – the butterflies that have come to take a look at her flowers.

Can you give the picture some pretty colours?

Rainy Day Fun

It's raining outside today, so Minnie and her friends are staying indoors.

1 Minnie has made colourful models of her friends.

Draw a line to link each model to the friend.

a   b   c   d

Donald

Mickey

Pluto

Goofy

2

Minnie's friends are busy doing some knitting.

Follow the paths from the balls of wool to find out what they each plan to knit.

Fairground Favourites

It's time to have some fun at the fair!

Minnie was filled with excitement when a big travelling fairground came to town.

"Oh, Mickey, let's go! I just love fairgrounds, the rides are sooooo much fun," she cried.

"Sure!" said Mickey. The two mice quickly gathered their friends and they all set off together.

First, Minnie wanted to go on the beautiful old Carousel.

"The Carousel is my favourite ride of all," she said, as she hopped up onto one of the horses.

"I love this ride the best because the horses are painted with such pretty colours." Mickey waved at Minnie as her horse gracefully went round and round in time to the music.

Next, Minnie suggested they go on the Big Dipper, but Mickey wasn't so sure – he thought it looked a bit scary!

"Oh, no, the Big Dipper isn't scary," said Minnie, as they joined the queue to go on the ride. "In fact, it's my favourite because it's really fast and super-whizzy!"

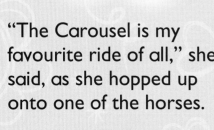

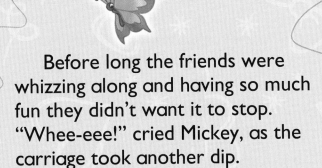

Before long the friends were whizzing along and having so much fun they didn't want it to stop. "Whee-eee!" cried Mickey, as the carriage took another dip.

When the ride finished they all felt a bit dizzy and in need of a rest!

"Perhaps we should find a nice relaxing ride to go on next," suggested Mickey.

"Good idea," said Minnie. She thought for a moment and then smiled. "I know just the one!"

Minnie took her friends over to a huge Ferris Wheel, which was covered in twinkly fairy lights.

"The Ferris Wheel is my favourite ride," said Minnie, as they neared the very top. "Look, you can see for miles from up here!"

When it was nearly time to go home, Mickey felt confused. "Hey, Minnie, the Ferris Wheel can't be your favourite ride because you said the Big Dipper was your favourite ... and before that you said the Carousel was your favourite," he said. "Which ride do you really like better than the others?"

Minnie blushed. "Well, I suppose the answer is ... ALL the rides are my favourites!"

"I see," laughed Mickey. "Well, do you know what, Minnie? I don't think I have a favourite fairground ride. But I do have a favourite mouse ... and that's you!"

"Oh, Mickey, you say my most favourite things!" Minnie laughed, as she took Mickey's arm and they headed home.

The End

Leading Lady

Minnie is Mickey's favourite mouse! Can you spot six differences between the two pictures?

Colour a heart shape each time you spot a difference!

Answers on page 68.

Dazzling Jewels

Minnie loves wearing sparkly rings that catch the light. Which one will she wear today?

Match the shape and colour she is thinking of to the right ring.

red

a

b

c

d

Then trace over the shapes below.

Answer on page 68.

Diamond   **Circle**   **Triangle**

63

Together Forever

Can you solve these romantic puzzles?

1

Photo 1

Photo 2

Which photo is each of the four details taken from?

a   b   c   d

2 Pluto has a letter for Minnie and Mickey. Can you guide him through the maze to reach them?

Start

3 How many kisses has Minnie given Mickey?

Count the lipstick marks and write the number in the heart.

Trail to my Heart

Can you help Mickey find the way to Minnie's heart?

Start

Trace a trail with your finger across the grid of love hearts, using only the pink hearts.

You can move across, up and down.

Answer on page 68.

Answers

Page 10
Minnie's Friends
Donald.

Page 12
Two by Two

Page 14
The New Puppy
11 paw prints.

Page 16
Happy Faces
1 – d, 2 – a,
3 – b, 4 – c.

Page 17
Find a Friend

Page 20
Passion For Fashion
Pattern Crazy
- d.
Bags Galore - d.

Page 22
Minnie's Dress
Dress d.

Page 24
Colourful Accessories
a – 3, b – 4,
c – 2, d – 5.

Page 28
Fashion Shoot
a and d.

Page 32
Draw the Fruits
1 – banana,
2 – orange,
3 – lemon,
4 – apple,
orange, lemon,
banana.

Page 34
What's Cooking?
a and e, b and f,
c and g.
d doesn't have
a match.

Page 35
Cute Cakes

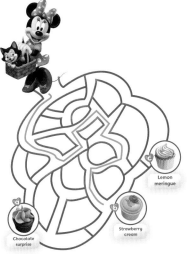

Strawberry
cream.

Page 36
Foodie Favourites
1. d. 2. d. 3.
Biggest – c,
smallest – d.
4. d.

Page 38
Dance Class
The musical
notes are red.

Page 41
Nice Moves
1 – b, 2 – d,
3 – a.

Answers

Page 42
Dance Partners

Page 47
Sport Crazy
Bows – 2,
hats – 1,
pom-poms
– 4.

Page 50
Places to Go
1 – c, 2 – d,
3 – a, 4 – b.

Page 51
On the Move
There are
10 roses.

Page 52
Minnie's Day
1. Minnie.
2. A bow.
3. Peach.

Page 56
Colourful Flowers
a – 2, b – 3,
c – 2, d – 3.

Page 58
Rainy Day Fun
1. a – Pluto,
b – Goofy,
c – Donald,
d – Mickey.
2. Mickey – a
sock, Goofy
– a scarf,
Daisy – a
jumper.

Page 62
Leading Lady

Page 63
Dazzling Jewels
Ring d.

Page 64
Together Forever
1. a – photo 1,
b – photo 2,
c – photo 2,
d – photo 1.

2.

3. Six kisses.

Page 66
Trail to my Heart

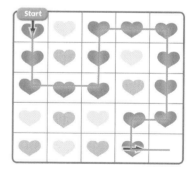